KING COBRA

THE bursting of a huge dam in Arizona led to high level night work among Manhattan skyscrapers for King Cobra, deadly foe of organised crime and crook-catcher extraordinary. His amazing snakeskin suit enabled him to cling to walls . . .

Would it not be more simple to kill Bronki? We've paid him plenty to take the rap for the Zuni Dam fiasco but—

H'mm! That sounds interesting. My tip-off was right.

4

John Bronki! I've hit paydirt.

They're going to that car—Hulloa! There's another car coming up.

U.S. Customs! What's going on here?

We are Federal Agents. Weren't you warned of this operation?

The supposed Customs men whipped out submachine guns, and got the drop on the lawmen.

You bet we were, G-men. Stand back! Leggo of Mr Bronki.

8

9

Hold the light steady and—Got it!

There's a chance the guard wouldn't hear my shot amongst all the other gunfire!

The guard—and he's fast asleep!

Sleep well now! By the time you wake up, I'll be well away!

Kendal was spotted by other tribesmen.

Look! The Feringhee escapes!

After several hours' hard riding, Lieutenant Kendal met Captain Stanners and the relief column.

On the outskirts of the village . . .

He mustn't get away, Hakmar!

No, don't shoot! He is out of range anyway— but he'll bring others to avenge the garrison! We will be waiting—and kill them all!

13

15

16

ACE OF SPACE

2200 AD. From outer space had come the Zargans, intent on adding the Earth to their list of conquered planets. In the forefront of the fighter craft which turned back the invaders was Bredan Douglas, ace pilot. Now a Wing-Commander, he was leading the space force which was out to sweep the Zargans from the occupied planets.

Jolan was Bredan's navigator.

That finished the Zargan air-cover on Aurila, Bredan. Now the Allied land-forces can move in. What's our next objective?

We're liberating Paldon—but that's not going to be easy, Jolan. The Zargans have concentrated their top space-force there.

Satellite docking-stations have been set-up around Paldon. We are to get our space-fleet here for briefing with Commander Clarke. If we can take Paldon, the rest of the occupied planets will fall, like nine-pins.

B

Within a few hours, all Bredan's squadrons were docked around Paldon.

You did a first-class job on the Zargan air support around Aurila, Douglas. The ground forces are already moving in.

Thanks. It will be a major conflict up here, Commander Clarke. This is where the Zargans will make their last stand . . .

The desperate Zargan High Command was in session on Paldon.

A little later a Zargan came on the Earth satellite video screen.

Karlon, Merlon, then Aurila! Now the Earth forces gather for one last battle. Why do we not attack at once?

Because their space-fighter wing is led by Bredan Douglas! We cannot beat him by armed force alone. He and his men are too good for us. Cunning and subtlety are needed. I have a plan that could defeat him!

. . . it is a challenge that Douglas might have the courage to accept. But here is Commander Zenko to issue the challenge himself . . .

Zenko! I've come up against him. He's their best fighter pilot! What's this all about?

We are both ace fighter pilots, Douglas, revelling in single combat. We could end this war—by a fight to the death, victory going to the forces' side of the winner. We use only conventional lasers. I will give you a rendezvous. If you do not appear, Douglas, I can only assume you are afraid—which would be a big boost to Zargan morale . . .

But it makes sense, Commander. This duel could save thousands of lives.

I forbid such an action. Douglas! Forget it!

And what if you lose, Douglas?

I won't lose! I know Zenko's style and I say it's worth the gamble.

Bredan stormed out. Stagman, a young squadron-leader, turned to Clarke.

Zenko's right, Commander. If Bredan doesn't show it'll be real morale-booster for the Zargans. But let me go in Bredan's place. If Zenko gets me then you announce that it wasn't Bredan and that the agreement doesn't stand. If I win, then no one need know it wasn't Bredan, except Bredan himself!

I'm keeping you, and your craft, under guard until well after that deadline is passed, Douglas. You're not—repeat NOT—fighting that crazy duel!

Hmmm . . . you've always fancied Bredan's laurels haven't you, Stagman. But it's not a bad idea . . .

Bredan gave a briefing on satellite defence, in case of Zargan attack.

I believe we should attack first, men, but the Zargans may not give us the chance. So this is my plan . . .

Bredan headed for Commander Clarke's office.

Commander—what's going on? Why is Stagman kitting-out for a solo?

Jolan took Bredan aside . . .

You ought to know, Bredan—Stagman is heading for the kitting-out chamber. He's going on a solo flight.

But, why should he— Hey! Wait a minute!

It's not your concern, Douglas. You've other work to do.

20

Moments later.

There goes Stagman! Won't those Zargans get a surprise if he can get Zenko and they discover they've lost their ace, and Bredan is still active.

Bredan settled at his craft's controls.

Zargan control—let's have those co-ordinates for the rendezvous with Zenko. It's 10-M units space-time exactly.

Suddenly . . . .

Locked-in to the co-ordinates Bredan approached the rendezvous.

There's Zenko! Ten-to-one he'll open up with a head-on chicken run. I'm banking on him sticking by his promise to use only conventional laser-weapons . . .

What—Aargh! My eyes! He has built-in a bank of lights! I'm blinded!

Bredan pulled up and away as Zenko fired a laser blast—just wide.

Bredan completed his turn, and . . .

That's fixed those lights! Now we'll have to fight clean—

Aaagh! He's ejecting his water-supply! It's turning to ice immediately!

Must get out of the way—that ice will impact like a shell!

He's missed again—but so much for a straight fight. Zenko's thrown away the rule book.

22

HURRICANE HUTCH

Penalty, ref!

HURRICANE HUTCH HUTCHISON and his pal, wily little Ollie Peake were on tour in the United States with English First Division Midford City. They were playing the Western Cougars, of Carseville, in a friendly game. Hutch, the beefy, good-natured striker only became a soccer hurricane when he got angry, and it was Ollie's job to set him alight . . . The Cougars knew all the dirty tricks.

What's the matter, Limey? Got lead in your boots?

That was a penalty, ref! You must have seen that big goon pulling on Hutch's jersey!

I seen nothing, bud! Get on with the game!

That ref's a crook! That was an obvious foul!

Take it easy, Ollie! You have to accept home-town refereeing! After all, it's only a friendly!

27

29

Just before half-time . . .
GOOOAAAALL! Bear City! Go! Go! Go!

Never mind the cheer-leaders, Hutch! Follow the game!

Two to the Bears! Go Bears, go!

Half-time! I wonder . . ! Maybe I can still get the big lummox going!

Take the Stetson and pretend you're Bear City fans. Here's what I want you to do!

What can I do with Hutch? He's day-dreaming. He gave away that goal.

The Bears kicked off—

I just hope my idea works!

Ollie got hold of Hutch's stetson, and had a word with some United fans, from England.

A big hat for a big-headed Hutch! Hey, Big Head!

Hey, look, Hutch. The Bear City supporters have got your Stetson!

WHAAT? They'll mess it up!

30

31

Hutch charged up and down the pitch, defending and attacking.

The big Limey plays all positions at once. Guess that's why he's called Hurricane—he storms around!

It took Hutch three more goals to work his annoyance out of his system.

All the goals were beauties!

Our fans did a good job. Now he's got his Stetson back!

I got a little bit peeved, Ollie! I shouldn't have let it go to my head!

Hats usually do! And that Stetson really suits you, Hutch!

The End

32

THE FIGHTING ROLLS

Kill all Sum-Ling's men! Destroy all those who oppose us!

LEE-FONG, a Chinese warlord, had got hold of a Rolls Royce Silver Ghost car and fitted it with a machine-gun. Now he was using it to wipe out his rivals . . .

C

35

40

Rolls-Royce 1914 Admiralty Turreted Pattern. Weight 3.5 tons. Speed 50 m.p.h. 8 mm. armour. One Vickers-Maxim m.g. 50 h.p. engine.

Sizaire-Berwick R.N.A.S. Armoured Car Division, 1915. Sunbeam 110 h.p. aero engine, rear-mounted. One Vickers-Maxim m.g., forward-firing. Known as the Wind Waggon.

ARMOURED CARS

Austin Armoured Car, Type 2. World War 1's most produced model. Weight 4.14 tons. Speed 35 m.p.h. 8 mm. armour. Twin turrets, with Hotchkiss m.g. Austin 50 h.p. engine. Range 150 miles.

Crossley 30/70 h.p. Chassis, 1930. Ground-to-air wireless equipment. Six wheels, spares carried on each side. Four alternative turret gun-mountings. Weight 7.12 tons. Speed 50 m.p.h. Crossley 70 b.h.p. engine. Vickers m.g.

Humber Mark 2. Weight 7.1 tons. Armour 15 mm. Speed 45 m.p.h. One 37 mm. gun, one Besa m.g. Rootes 90 b.p.h. engine. Range 250 miles.

A.E.C. Mark 3. Weight 12.7 tons. Speed 40 m.p.h. 30 mm. armour. One 75 mm. gun, one Besa m.g. Range 250 miles.

MOB

... A BUNCH OF HIGHLY TRAINED SOLDIERS WILLING TO GO ANYWHERE, DO ANY JOB... AS LONG AS THE PRICE IS RIGHT! IN THE TRUCIAL STATE OF QARA, THEY'VE BEEN HIRED TO PUT DOWN A REVOLT AGAINST THE EMIR....

YEEAARRGH!

Sheikh Sayid and his lieutenants are prisoners, Colonel Amair—the rest of the rebels are running.

The Emir will be pleased, Morgan. What does not please him is having to arrest one of your men.

Tom was joined by two of his men, Yonkers and Mali—

Boys, it seems our mate Flynn was caught trying to flit with a bundle of treasure from the Emir's palace.

The no-good thief!

A week later, in the dungeon of Fort Qara—

Morgan, 'tis all a dreadful misunderstanding. I'll never be knowing how them pearls got into me pack.

Yeah, Flynn, you've been framed. The little people put 'em there. I've heard all these excuses before.

They hold the old fort—and they have taken captive the visitors from England. And your man Flynn is in charge!

Morgan drove to the Emir's palace.

I have been told what has happened. Morgan, a friend wishes to talk with you.

Morg, the price of the royal party is ten million pounds sterling in gold and an aircraft out of here. Otherwise you'll not see them alive again. The Emir's already agreed to my terms.

Agreeing to Flynn's terms doesn't mean you'll save the lives of your visitors, Emir—but I have a plan that might.

Proceed with your plan, Morgan, but let harm come to the English royal and my headsman's sword will finish you and your men.

That night, Morgan led out a waterborne raiding party—

There is the fort. Take us in against the wall. The gaoler let slip an interesting detail when I visited Flynn—there's an underwater entrance!

This is why we waited for low tide. This is a flood valve, lads. This is how water was let in to flood the armoury if a fire started among the kegs of black powder in the old days.

46

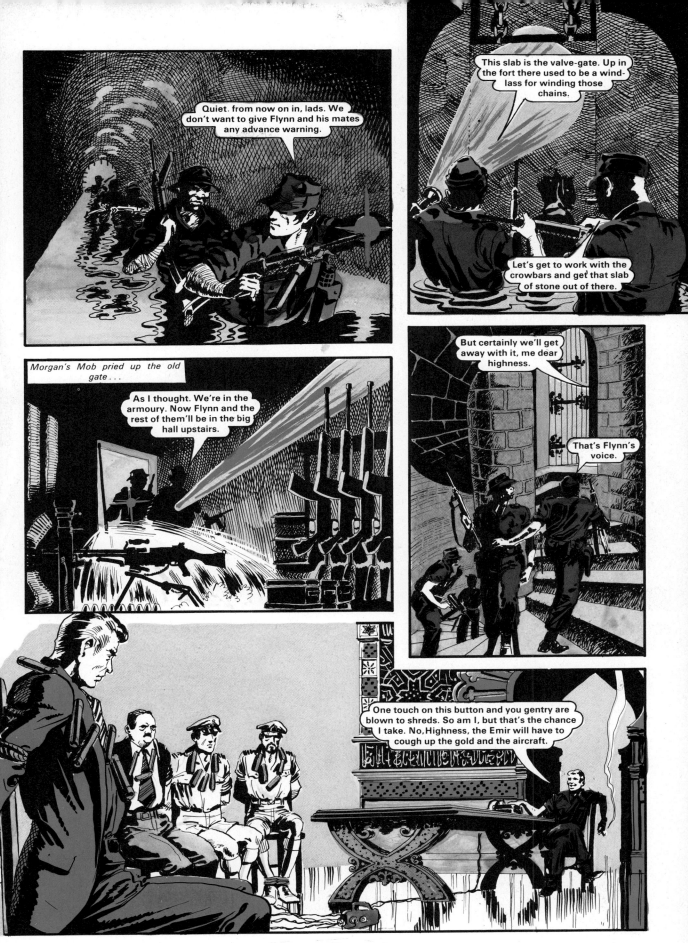

47

FLYING FURY

General Montgomery's desert army has built up its strength. Rommel's days in Egypt are numbered!

THE Western Desert, World War II. To 833 Squadron had come Sergeant-Pilot Fury, deadly in the air and very mysterious, aiding the Desert Air Force and the Eighth Army against German General Rommel and his Afrika Korps. Tank-busting Hurricanes and Hurribombers were out to surprise Nazi armour, while high above them Wellington bombers headed towards the German lines. Squadron-Leader Don Nixon commanded 833 Squadron.

D

54

During the day, preparations for the next joint fighter-bomber raid on Rommel's armour went ahead.

Now's my chance to fit the special radio transmitter. It will lead our Luftwaffe night fighters to the aircarft.

The spy activated the radio transmitter just before take-off.

Okay, sir—it's ready! Good luck!

The pilot suddenly showed his face.

Fury! No! You're dead—

Not yet, spy! I saw you after you threw the grenade. Is your transmitter working?

Two guns roared together.

Nnnnngh!

He missed, Nixon. I didn't! I'll check the plane and then take off.

Are you all right, Fury? We join the Wellington bombers as before.

Nixon had known about the trap set by Fury.

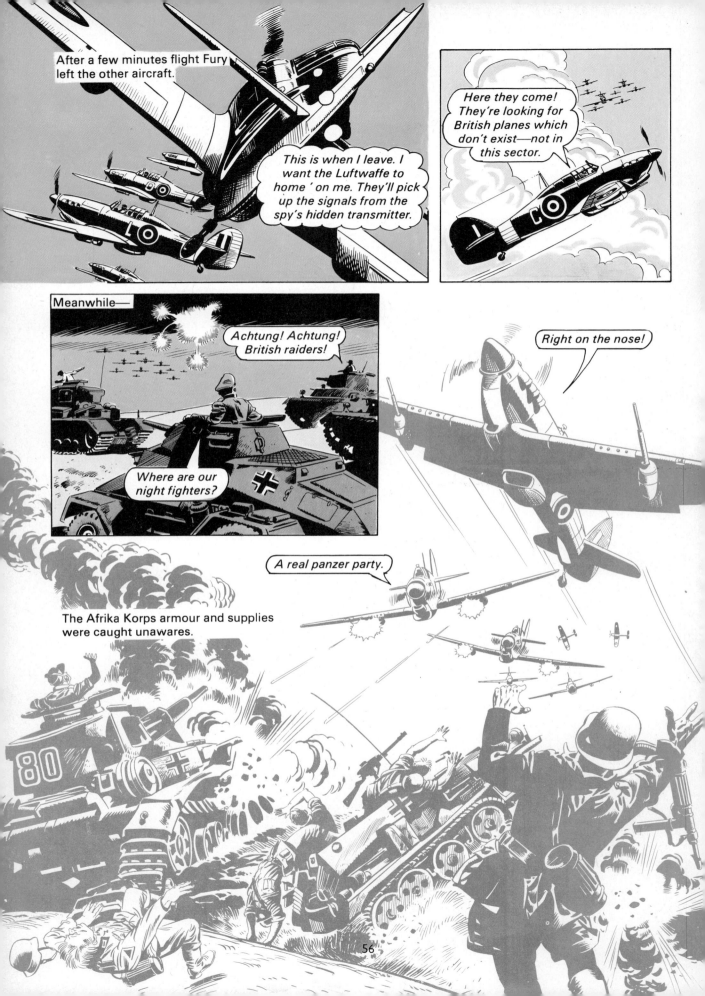

57

THEY FOUGHT IN WORLD WAR II

AMERICAN MARTIN BAKER 3

RUSSIAN MIG 7

ITALIAN SAVOIA MARCHETTI

JAPANESE NAKAJAMA 87

BRITISH BLACKBURN FIREBRAND 11

GERMAN MESSERSCHMITT " BF 109 "

FRENCH C.A.O. 200

The COONSKIN GRENADIER

ZEBADIAH FLOOD was a hillbilly from the Great Smokies of Carolina, a crackshot with his long, Daniel Boone rifle and a very unorthodox character. He was also, by ancient charter and warrant, an Honorary Colonel in the very plush English regiment the Royal Grenadiers, King George's Own, and a constant nightmare to the Colonel, Sir John Pelham. Already, in World War II, Zeb and Alexander the ape, the regimental mascot, had given Sir John many grey hairs.

You sit there nice and quiet, Alexander, while I pen a few lines to my Maw, back in Sassafras County, Carolina.

DEAR MAW. GOTTEN BACK TO ENGLAND AFTER SOME FEUDING WITH THEM SQUARE-HEAD YANKEES IN FURRIN PARTS.

Me an' Alexander, the mascot, an' the fire-eetin' Sarn't-Major Minchin . . .

I RECKON THE JOY OF SEEING US AGAIN WAS JUST TOO MUCH FER SIR JOHN THE DEPOT BOSS AT POTOMAC BARRACKS. P.T.O

No use . . . got to pancake . . .

So we landed . . . sort of . . .

Sidney, I still say these trees have no right to be here.

Your leg's broken, Albert. I'd better stay with you while the soldiers scout around for help.

Leave it to us Royal Grenadiers.

So off we traipsed . . .

Honorary Colonel— look! An 'ighway.

Maybe we can find where them fliers has landed us. Nice boys, but I wouldn't rely on either of 'em to locate his own elbow.

MARCHE 7Km   BASTOGNES 30Km

At least we is still in Europe—France or Belgium probably.

Look, Yankee soldier-boys!

Them Yankees was right ill-mannerly . . .

ROAD 'OGS!

Look up yonder, Sarn't-Major. A shack, on the hill them Yankees come down.

So we traipsed up to this ol' stone shack . . .

This is where them trucks come from, sure 'nuff.

Must be a Yankee 'eadquarters.

Cousin, we'd be obliged for some help. Are you in charge here?

I am Dufay, butler to the Count de Gallicos. Gentlemen, you may enter.

Kindly wait in this antechamber while I announce you to my master.

I'd better do the chatting, Honorary Colonel. I'm used to 'andling the haristocracy.

Looks like we are not the only visitors, Sarn't-Major.

Pardon, suh, but are you waiting to be announced to this Count Gallicos?

I am Count de Gallicos, my friend—basely imprisoned by my butler who turns out to be a Nazi!

Continued on Page 114

64

THE BATTLE OF JUTLAND

ON Saturday afternoon, June 21, 1919, in Scapa Flow, in the Orkney Islands to the north of Scotland, some schoolchildren saw, by chance, an amazing sight. On a sightseeing trip around the surrendered German High Seas Fleet, in the tug " Flying Kestrel," they witnessed the breath-taking spectacle of the once-mighty-fleet being scuttled by its caretaker crews. In all, eleven battleships, five battle cruisers, eight light cruisers and several destroyers went to the bottom. This was the tragic end to a story which had begun in the Spring of 1916, in World War 1.

E

The German High Seas Fleet and the British Grand Fleet had never met in full battle up to early 1916.

On May 30, the Secret German naval signal, "31 Gg 2490" readied its fleet of 100 ships and 45,000 men to set forth to lure out and destroy the British Navy.

The signal was intercepted by the British.

In the Schillig Roads, in the Jade Estuary, in Germany, Vice-Admiral Hipper's battle cruisers weighed anchor and led the German fleet to sea on May 31, 1916.

The British Grand Fleet needed only one single flag hoisted to ready all ships. From Scapa Flow, under Admiral Jellicoe, sailed battleships like " Iron Duke," " Royal Oak," " Vanguard" . . . From Rosyth under Vice-Admiral Beatty steamed battle cruisers such as " Lion," " Valiant," " Malaya " . . .

By 10.30 p.m. on May 30, the Grand Fleet was at sea, heading for a prepared rendezvous. There were 148 ships and 60,000 men and the North Sea was to be the battle-ground.

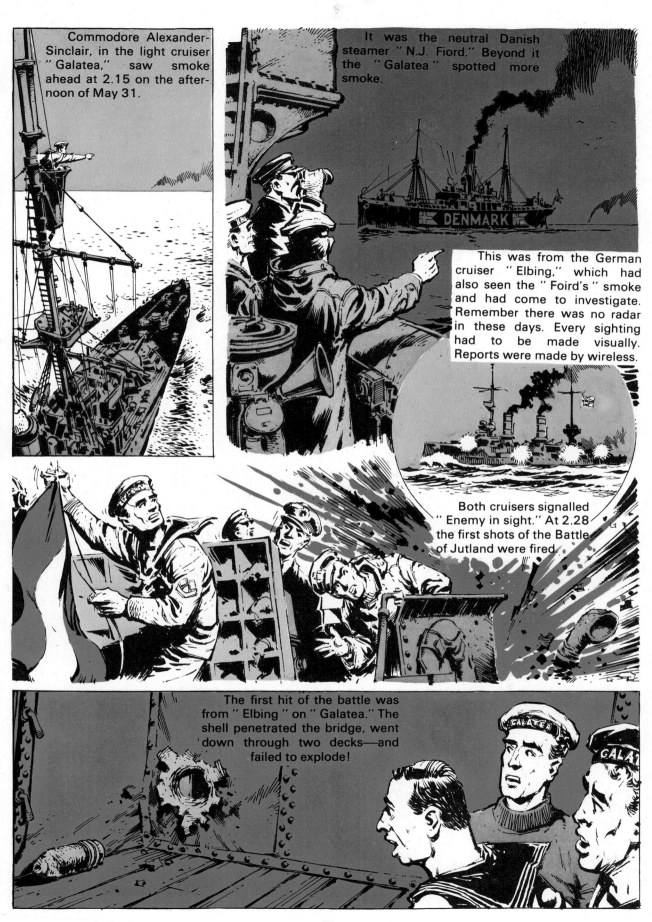

Commodore Alexander-Sinclair, in the light cruiser "Galatea," saw smoke ahead at 2.15 on the afternoon of May 31.

It was the neutral Danish steamer "N.J. Fiord." Beyond it the "Galatea" spotted more smoke.

This was from the German cruiser "Elbing," which had also seen the "Foird's" smoke and had come to investigate. Remember there was no radar in these days. Every sighting had to be made visually. Reports were made by wireless.

Both cruisers signalled "Enemy in sight." At 2.28 the first shots of the Battle of Jutland were fired.

The first hit of the battle was from "Elbing" on "Galatea." The shell penetrated the bridge, went down through two decks—and failed to explode!

At 3.29 " Galatea " reported more smoke beyond the enemy light cruisers, and bugles sounded " Action Stations " in the Grand Fleet battle cruiser squadrons. At 18,000 yards their guns opened fire.

The first British hit was by the " Queen Mary," champion gunnery ship of the Grand Fleet. Two of her shells smashed a gun turret on the " Sydlitz." She then targetted on the " Derfflinger."

A shell from the " Lutzow " burst through the midship turret of the " Lion " and started a fire which endangered the whole ship.

The turret officer, Major Harvey of the Marines, ordered his turret to be flooded. He and his surviving men died but the ship was saved. Harvey was awarded a posthumous Victoria Cross.

Under fire from the "Sydlitz" and the "Derfflinger," the "Queen Mary" blew up. The "Tiger," following closely behind, had to take violent avoiding action.

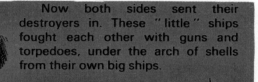

Now both sides sent their destroyers in. These "little" ships fought each other with guns and torpedoes, under the arch of shells from their own big ships.

The British destroyers chased off their opposite numbers, then came under fire from the German battle cruisers. The "Seydlitz" was hit by a torpedo but survived. The British destroyers "Nomad" and "Nestor" were sunk. Commander Bingham of the "Nestor" won the V.C.

All through the night, sections of the two mighty fleets clashed, struck deadly blows and reeled apart again.

The British light cruiser "Chester" was ambushed by four German ships, "Frankfurt," "Weisbaden," "Pillau" and "Elbing." "Chester," badly damaged, led them under the guns of British battle cruisers. On the "Chester," sixteen-year-old Boy First Class Jack Cornwall, mortally wounded, fought his six-inch gun until he was the last man on his feet. He won a posthumous V.C.

The German battle cruiser "Lutzow" was so crippled by gunfire that Vice-Admiral Hipper, and his staff transferred to the torpedo boat G39, leader of the First Half Flotilla.

With his entire German High Seas Fleet facing potential disaster, Vice-Admiral Scheer flung his four remaining, damaged, battle cruisers into a death charge at the British Grand Fleet, to cover his other ships as they turned away from the enemy.

The German High Seas Fleet finally limped home, licking its wounds, and even as it neared harbour, the battleship "Ostfriesland" was hit by a British mine. However, the two tremendous enemy fleets had never really got to grips.

The Battle of Jutland was highlighted by tremendous courage, on both sides, but overall it was an indecisive action because of lack of proper intelligence reports and confusing flag signals.

The two battle fleets never met again in any large encounters. On November 23, 1918, Sir David Beatty, then Commander-in-Chief, watched the British light cruiser "Cardiff" lead the surrendered German High Seas Fleet into the Firth of Forth. Later the German ships were escorted to Scapa Flow—where their last shameful act finally took place.

The End

72

73

Dead! But I know Carlini was murdered— and three people were behind it! This guy was the tool, killed to keep his mouth shut.

Later—

Quite a discovery, Herr Kestrel! Dreiberg will be surprised!

When you see him, Sivers, tell him I'm going to look over the dead guy's room in the village.

But when Kestrel reached the village—

Somebody up in that room is taking an interest in my arrival! If that's the dead guy's room—

Why such sudden interest? What has happened? There is one policeman up there already!

Ha! I've got him! The only cop who knows of the guy's death is Sivers, so that guy can't be a cop . . .

At the top of the stairs—

Ugh!

Go away! The police—

As Kestrel got to his feet—

Look out!

74

Looks like I was wrong about Dreiberg!

Seconds later—

He's staying calm. He's a cool one is Dreiberg . . . a good cop . . .

Soon they were up in the fresh air.

Th—thank you, Kestrel . . . I—I owe you my life . . .

And I owe you an apology and a new window pane!

You were right, Kestrel! Carlini's death was no accident! The enquiry is now a German one. You may return home.

It's all yours, chum! The guy who killed Carlini is dead and whoever killed him is the one who attempted to kill you. I'll leave tomorrow.

Some time later, in Kestrel's room.

You must feel badly about the fatal accidents at the Larnberg Circus, Herr Bluther.

Yes. I was a clown and I was a close friend of Carlini—who was not always a trapeze artist.

Hmmm! It could be worth delaying my trip to have a word with that old boy.

79

DANNY BOYD

Oh, what a beautiful morning! I'm stiff with sleeping under this boat, but I'll soon get limbered up!

DANNY BOYD, an up-and-coming young golf professional who had his European tournament ticket, was competing in the Portuguese Open at the Vasco Club at Algarva. Danny's mean manager Foxy Luter, had not paid for any accomodation for Danny and the lad was living rough. He was used to this, as he worked his way along the rough, tough road to stardom—which was what Danny was aiming at.

Brr! Just how I like my bath water—bloomin' freezing!

Golf came before food for Danny. He used his own method of grooving his swing. He sang his name to himself.

Oh, DA-N-N-Y B-O-Y-D!

Danny got up to the club house early.

There's coffee free to competitors. I'll go in and fill up.

The second day had been very windy and had sent the scores up.

Great! I'm 15th and the wind has dropped. Only one snag—looks like I'm out with Len Small again.

Len Small was another young pro. He knew every rule in the book, and he used them, to the absolute limit, both for, and against, any player.

Hi, Len! I see we're out together again. Got your rule book, then?

Right here in my pocket, Danny. Never move without it!

81

Danny spoke no Spanish and the caddies spoke only a few words of English. But the sardines helped Danny to make friends.

Two days later the Championship started. Danny was playing with Aldo Garaddo, one of the top Spanish players.

Garaddo's putt for a birdie at the first hole stopped right on the lip of the hole.

Tough luck, Aldo!

Garaddo did a strange thing. He stood between his ball and the blazing sun.

In a few seconds the grass wilted—and the ball fell into the hole.

I'm sure that must be against the rules, Aldo.

I cast my shadow, the grass wilts and bends, my ball falls. I see no rule against!

Danny had a 74, two over par. He spent the rest of the day on the practice ground. Next morning.

The caddies are playing some game with a 7 iron, a ball and an old can. Looks like fun.

Danny asked to join in.

Senor, we play for money.

Well, I don't gamble so anything I win, I'll give back to you.

Not much of a lie, this gravel path. Still, the caddies make it look easy.

86

Danny played, using an open club face. He missed the can.

That will cost you two pesetas, senor.

Danny soon lost his few pesetas. The caddies were very accurate with chip shots off rough ground.

Danny studdied the caddies' technique.

Now I get it. You hit the ball, with a closed club face, before you hit the gravel on the road!

Si, senor!

I've got it! This is the way to play the shot!

Suddenly, Danny realised what the time was.

Now I'm due on the tee. You've got all my money, but as a lesson it was worth the fee!

Danny rushed to the first tee, but . . .

You are six minutes late, senor.

I'm very sorry. What does that cost me? A fine?

Danny was disqualified. Foxy Luter was furious.

You young idiot! You can't win money to pay for my chalet. You can find your own way to Madrid for the next tournament.

Well, I learned some more today. I learned to play chip shots off gravel, I learned never to be late on the tee—and I learned that it's four hundred miles to Madrid!

The driver gave Danny a lift to Madrid, and offered to act as his caddy. At the Real Club, Danny discovered that Len Small was once more his partner.

Then the driver had a go.

Danny started brilliantly, and sang to his swing.

Danny did the first nine holes in 34 strokes.

Then at the tenth, Danny's ball failed to carry the lake.

Danny prepared to drop a ball opposite where the first ball had dropped into the water.

89

Danny played what was now his third shot—into the water again.

That was my own fault. By playing an old ball I was mentally expecting to land in the water.

Danny hit shot number five on to the green, and sank the putt for a six.

On the next tee, Danny was still thinking about the last hole.

A six at a par three. I must get a birdie here. I'll cut across the corner. Oh, blow!

Danny lost the ball. Once again he tried to cut the corner—and failed.

The hole finally cost Danny nine shots.

Boyd needed that putt to avoid double figures!

Danny finished on 81. The leader was round in 66.

Bad luck, Danny.

Not bad luck, bad temper! I threw away seven shots in two holes, because I didn't keep cool.

Danny scored 70 on the second day, but failed to beat the cut—by one shot!

So once again Danny took to the road.

I've got to get to Rome for the Italian Open. I've a week to get there—no money—no food, and no sign of Foxy Luter. But I'm still going to be a professional golfer—and a good one!

The End

90

1969 July 20. A historic moment for mankind as Neil Armstrong becomes the first man to walk on the moon's surface. Yet little did the watching millions know that the Apollo 11 mission nearly ended in disaster before it even began . . .

The ORGANISATION

Florida, U.S.A., July 16. Joe Bannon was a used-car salesman.

Yeah, it's a nice lookin' car, but the price . . .

Oh, hurry up, Jack, make up your mind. We're gonna miss the moonshot launch!

He'll take it. I can always . . . Hey! My ring is activated! "O" wants me. I'll nip in to the office.

But he was also a member of the Organisation, a world-wide secret organisation pledged to uphold law and order and freedom—with their lives if necessary. Each member wore a special ring which could call them for action.

"O" calling. Priority Red! Report of a sabotage attempt on Apollo II moon launch. You are to link up with our man in the field . . .

Seconds later . . .

Sorry, sir. Can't wait for you. I've got other work to do.

B . . . but . . .

Bannon sped along the State highway.

" O " information is that Green Brigade terrorists are planning to blast Apollo II with a ground-to-air missile. They've holed up a few miles inland from the launch area.

Minutes later, on a side dirt track.

Get on my battle kit now. Morgan, my fellow agent, should be around here somewhere. Hey—shots!

What . . . ? Look out!

Let's see how you face up to hot lead!

Got 'em both!

Morgan? How are you?

I'm done for, but no matter. Gotta stop them firing that missile. Look over the edge of the cliff. They've set everything up. I almost got to them, but—

Six terrorists. I'd never get them all. Must draw them off—somehow.

Look—another intruder!

Shenk, Petro—after him.

C'mon, Morgan —got to get back to the car.

The car— but why?

This track runs to the top of the hill. If I can get up enough speed and go right over and land on top of the missile, it'll set if off. And if I can bale out in time—

No chance, Bannon, but I'll do it. Get me into the driver's seat.

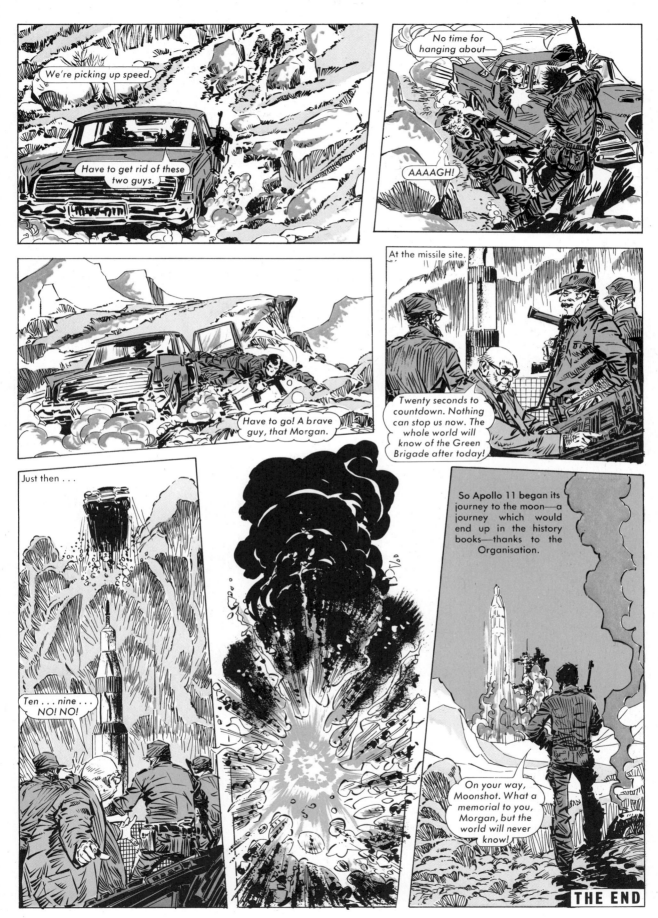

ONCE A JOLLY SWAGMAN

JIM WADE was a swagman, the name given to men who wandered the Outback of Australia in the early 1900s, looking for work. With Jim travelled young Will Machin, an orphan boy, with his dog, Butch. Times were hard and jobs few and far between, but Will had managed to get hold of one of the new-fangled motor-bikes, which made their travelling easier. Now, on a dirt road in the bush they came across a strange sight.

I've heard of working like a horse, Will, but this is ridiculous!

Too right, Swaggie. We'll see what the poor joker is up to.

Work like that can kill a horse, mate, let alone a bloke!

I know—it just killed my old horse! Dropped down dead ten miles back, he did!

Tommy Phelan's my name. There's a Bush Week Fair at Wyalkatchem and I was going to make money with my merry-go-round, but now—

We still might be able to help the poor joker, Swaggie. Butch, have a bit cheese.

We'll use my motorcycle to haul yer to Wyalkatchem and then we'll use it to drive the merry-go-round. You can give us half-shares in the takings. How about it?

Yer on, sports— half-shares it is.

Half the takings! Huh, they must think I'm barmy!

They finally reached Wyalkatchem, a small outback township.

Hey, lookit that! Tommy Phelan's motorised his merry-go-round!

Can I have a go on it, Dad? Can I—eh? —can I?

G

103

BERTIE'S BEAR

JUNE 1944, in World War II. In Italy, the Allied troops had occupied Rome and the Nazis were on the retreat. Italy had signed an armistice. With the triumphant 4th. Fusiliers were country boy Private Bert Toomly and Bozzler—the regimental mascot—a wild and very unusual bear which had adopted Bert in the regiment's Burma campaign. Now there was to be a triumphal parade.

Come on, Bozzler! Got to smarten you up for the parade. Colonel Crumpton wants to show off the Regimental Colours.

The bear's a lot tidier than you, Bert.

Head up, Bozz! No— not up on your hind legs!

Viva! Viva! A bear! Orso!

Colonel Crumpton was not pleased.

Who brought that bear, sergeant?

Private Toomly, sir! Our mascot—er, not Toomly, the bear!

Where are you going now, Bozz? Stone me, Jerries everywhere! Gun-teams and all! They'll be able to blast anything that moves on the road.

Bert was a deadly shot.

Our blokes will be following up, Bozz, so we can't let 'em be ambushed!

The bear vanished—and Germans appeared.

One man! Hey! A dummkopf!

Hey! I know what that means!

Yeeek! Bozz! What are you playing at?

Ain't on me own! My mates are everywhere!

That we will soon know!

Are you a scout? Is your main force coming along the road?

Get lost! All I tell you is a name and number!

SHIP SHAPES

THIS is the "Voltaire" of the Lamport and Holt Lines of the 1930's. Typical cargo vessel of the time, converted from the then-unprofitable New York—South America service to the new, cheap, cruises which became popular. "Voltaire" was 13,000 tons, straight stem, tall funnel, with long, open, promenade and boat decks. Did the Norwegian fiords, on 12 to 13 day trips. The advertising posters of these cruises, done by well-known marine artists of the day, became sought-after works of art.

Then... ..and Now

A COMPOSITE example of the modern, specially-built, cruise ship, used by different nations. Four engines, geared in pairs to twin screws, 20 knots, 17,500 tons, 750 passengers. Funnel well aft, to keep exhaust gases clear of passengers. Stabilised fin for comfort at sea. Observation lounge higher than navigation bridge. Boats power-driven and act as launches to ferry passengers ashore when needed. Fitted with cinemas, discos, swimming pools—a floating first-class hotel. Operate all over the world, from Equator to Antartica.

H

115

So of we rid...

Woah! This is hurtin' my—er—dignity!

Regardez, below us! The American fuel dump!

Then we seen something else...

The Boche blitz unit! We have no time to reach the Americans.

There's one way of reaching 'em, Count.

That is the alarm! What hit the old shell case?

But the Boche are disguised. Those at the fuel dump will think they are fellow Americans.

Then we gotta stop them reaching that dump, Count.

So I done me some shooting...

116

I caused a proper pile-up . . .

A remarkable shot with a remarkable weapon, my friend.

Just an ol' Dan'l Boone pea-rifle, Count.

Now to warm up this clambake!

Them real Yankees got the wrong notion . . .

Our boys are being fired on from the hill.

Must be some Kraut infiltrators! We were warned to watch for them.

The fake Yankees was gettin' real riled . . .

Himmel, we must go in afoot. Follow me . . .

Forward! The Americans do not suspect us—argh!

117

The End

122

Then, in a tremendous breakaway, Dozy Danny scored the equaliser.

In the second half, Danny scored a brilliant second, and winning goal.

The second game was in Barcelona.

They're football-mad here. The technical college team will be a cracker.

How will we get rid of the Principal this time? I wonder what Cedric has dreamed up?

Ole! I got the purser to give Uncle Albert a free ticket for the bull fight. There's only one snag, he's going in the same bus as we're using. Any ideas, lads?

Danny went ashore as a " sailor "

That disguise wouldn't fool a blind man.

It's good enough to fool Uncle Albert.

In the dressing-room.

I'm keeping my beard on. I quite like it—

Get that fungus off, you idiot!

Almost on the final whistle, Danny was brought down in the penalty area . . .

The penalty was given.

Dozy Danny took the kick—and Teesdale had won their second game.

In the Mediterranean, the Teesdale side kept fit by playing deck games.

We're playng a team from Monaco in the final, at Monte Carlo. The Principal is sure to attend that game, Cedric, so—

It's a problem, but I'm working on it, Danny.

Danny's luck ran out, finally.

Steward! Dean! What—what are you doing here on board?

I'm a steward, sir. Can I get you anything?

The Teesdale boys were unhappy.

Now that the Principal knows about Danny, he's got no chance of playing.

Worse than that, he's asked the captain to confine Danny to ship while we're at Monte Carlo.

Leave it to me, lads. I've got friendly with the ship's wireless operator. He has a cousin in the palace at Monaco, so—

I know, you're going to get your uncle knighted, Cedric. Here, have my ice cream. You're a good lad.

125

Monte Carlo is a tiny independent state, ruled by Prince Rainier.

Look! Here comes Prince Rainier's launch.

Cedric did get through to the palace. I wonder what Cedric's friend has wangled.

The palace official had an invitation for Principal Nablas.

Summoned to the palace to be presented to Prince Rainier and Princess Grace! I'll be delighted.

At Monte Carlo, the S.S. Kenya anchored outside the harbour. The passengers went ashore in launches.

Careful with that hamper, Jim.

You bet, we don't want our gear to fall in the sea, do we!

Okay, Danny, the Principal's headed for the palace. You can come out now.

Thank goodness. I was getting that shut-in feeling.

The palace overlooked the football stadium.

At first, the Monaco players were all over the Teesdale team.